The Alphabet

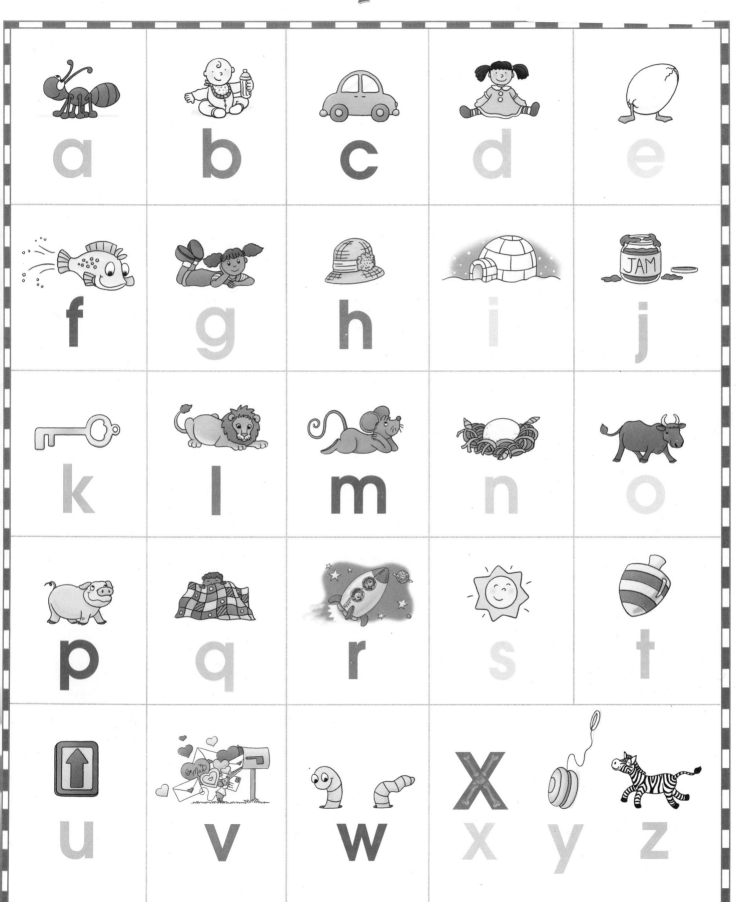

a	b	c	d	e
f	g	h	i	j
k	l	m	n	o
p	q	r	s	t
u	v	w	x	y	z

a

animals

Trace over a. Then write a.

a a a a a a a a a a a a a a a a a a

Write a to finish the picture words.

h a t

a nt

a

was an **apple**
That fell from a tree;
A worm that was in it
Waved to me.

Trace over **a**. Then write **a**.

Write **a** to begin each word.
Draw a line from the picture to the picture word.

_____ **pple**

_____ **pron**

_____ **ngel**

b

bird

Trace over **b**. Then write **b**.

Write **b** to finish the picture words.

ba___y

___ear

b

was a **bee**

Who flew upside down;

When he would smile

It looked like a frown.

Trace over **b**. Then write **b**.

Write **b** to begin two words. Write **b** to end a word.
Draw a line from the picture to the picture word.

_____ all

_____ utterfly

we _____

C

camel

Trace over c. Then write c.

Write c to finish the picture words.

_at

_ar

6

C

was a **cat**

Who went out every night;

He didn't come home

Until dawn's early light.

Trace over c. Then write c

Write c to begin each word.
Draw a line from the picture to the picture word.

_____ ake

_____ ow

_____ arrot

d
dog

Trace over **d**. Then write **d**.

Write **d** to finish the picture words.

oll

be

8

d

was a **dog**;

In the morning he howled;

He woke up a bear

Who grumbled and growled.

Trace over **d**. Then write **d**.

Write **d** to begin two words. Write **d** to end a word.
Draw a line from the picture to the picture word.

_____ og

_____ inosaur

bir _____

e

elephant

Trace over e. Then write e.

Write e to finish the picture words.

e g g

b e l l

10

e was an **elephant**

With really big feet;

The animals scattered

As he walked down the street.

Trace over e. Then write e.

Write e to begin each word.
Draw a line from the picture to the picture word.

_____ lephant

_____ gg

_____ nvelope

f

fox

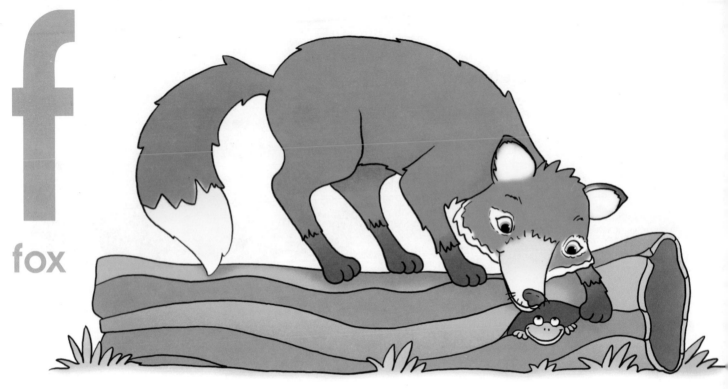

Trace over f. Then write f.

Write f to finish the picture words.

___ish

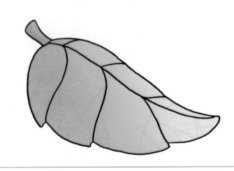

___lea___

12

f was a **fish**

Who felt he was sick;

He knitted a jumper

That was cosy and thick.

Trace over **f**. Then write **f**.

Write **f** to begin two words. Write **f** to end a word.
Draw a line from the picture to the picture word.

_____ **ish**

_____ **ox**

el _____

g

goose

Trace over **g**. Then write **g**.

Write **g** to finish the picture words.

 irl

 pi

14

g

was a **goat**

With two curly horns;

He's been full of mischief

Since the day he was born.

Trace over **g**. Then write **g**.

Write **g** to begin two words. Write **g** to end a word.
Draw a line from the picture to the picture word.

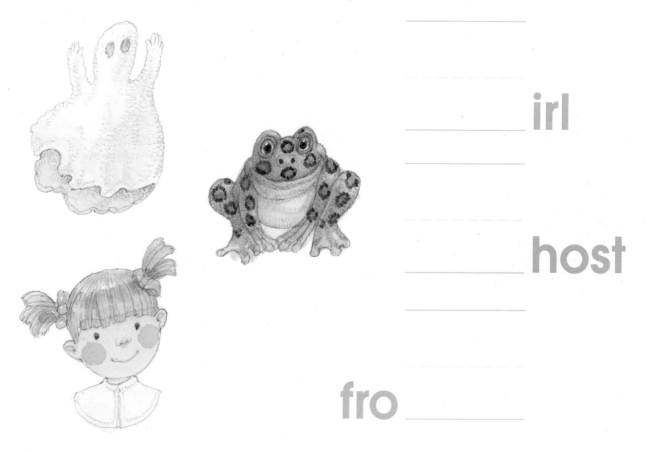

_____irl

_____host

fro_____

h

helmets

Trace over **h**. Then write **h**.

h

Write **h** to finish the picture words.

at

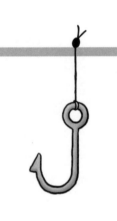

ook

h

was a **hat**

So tall and so green;

Birds nested in it

And couldn't be seen.

Trace over **h**. Then write **h**.

Write **h** to begin each word.
Draw a line from the picture to the picture word.

_____ en

_____ eart

_____ orse

i

insects

Trace over **i**. Then write **i**.

Write **i** to finish the picture words.

f__sh

__gloo

18

i was an **itch**

That bothered a bear;

He scratched and he scratched

Till he lost all his hair.

Trace over **i**. Then write **i**.

2
1

Write **i** to begin each word.
Draw a line from the picture to the picture word.

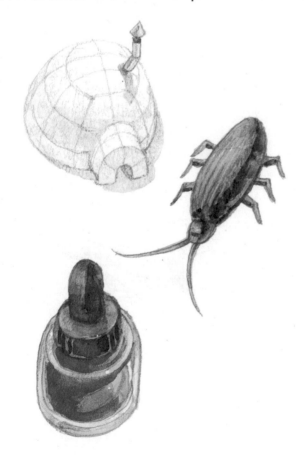

_____ nk

_____ nsect

_____ gloo

j

jaguar

Trace over j. Then write j.

j

Write j to finish the picture words.

___am

___et

j

was a **jogger**
Who tried not to stop;
Around and around
He went in one spot.

Trace over j. Then write j.

Write j to begin each word.
Draw a line from the picture
to the picture word.

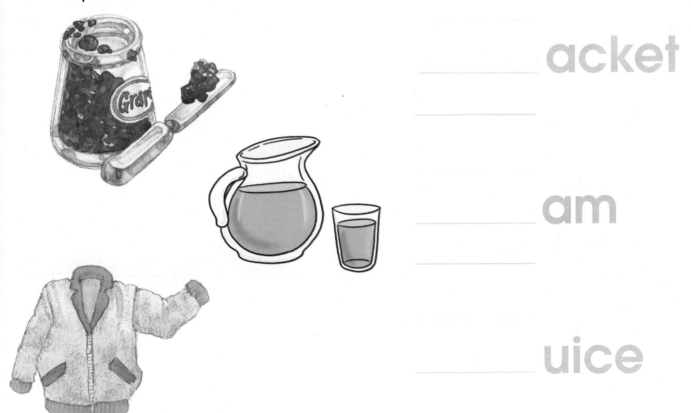

_____ acket

_____ am

_____ uice

k

kangaroos

Trace over k. Then write k.

Write k to finish the picture words.

___ ey

___ boo

was a **koala**

Who wanted to fly;

He made wings out of leaves

And flew in the sky.

Trace over k. Then write k.

Write k to begin two words. Write k to end a word.
Draw a line from the picture to the picture word.

_____ itten

_____ ey

duc _____

l

lizard

Trace over l. Then write l.

Write l to finish the picture words.

___ion

___ow

24

I was a **lion**

Who while asleep would snore;

The sound shook the walls

Of his neighbour next door.

Trace over I. Then write I.

Write I to begin two words. Write I to end a word.
Draw a line from the picture to the picture word.

_____ake

_____eaves

bel_____

m
moose

Trace over **m**. Then write **m**.

Write **m** to finish the picture words.

ouse

dru

m

was **Miss Molly** ,

Who turned in her toes

And hung down her head

Till her knees touched her nose.

Trace over **m**. Then write **m**.

Write **m** to begin two words. Write **m** to end a word.
Draw a line from the picture to the picture word.

_____ ittens

_____ oney

dru _____

n

numbers

Trace over **n**. Then write **n**.

n

Write **n** to finish the picture words.

fe__ce

__est

n

was a **newt**

Who bought a new boat,

So he could go skiing

With his friend the white goat.

Trace over **n**. Then write **n**.

Write **n** to begin two words. Write **n** to end a word.
Draw a line from the picture to the picture word.

_____et

_____

_____uts

_____

clow_____

O

octopus

Trace over o. Then write o.

Write o to finish the picture words.

___ x

s ___ ck

O

was an **owl**

Who kept saying 'Whooo!'

He met a fine cow

Who answered with 'Moo!'

Trace over o. Then write o.

Write o to begin each word.
Draw a line from the picture to the picture word.

_____ live

_____ wl

_____ x

p

penguins

Trace over **p**. Then write **p**.

Write **p** to finish the picture words.

___ig

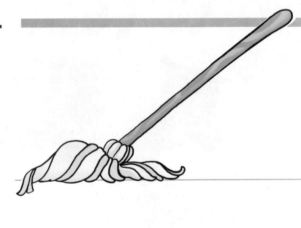

___mo___

p

was a **pig**
With a curly pink tail;
He ordered a straightener
That came in the mail.

Trace over p. Then write p.

Write p to begin two words. Write p to end a word.
Draw a line from the picture to the picture word.

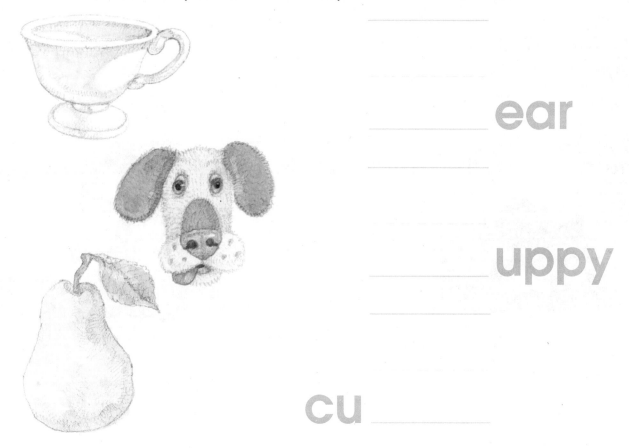

_____ear

_____uppy

cu _____

q

quail

Trace over **q**. Then write **q**.

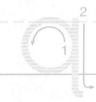

Write **q** to finish the picture words.

uilt

ueen

34

q

was a **quail**

Who lived in a tree;

She made tiny cookies

When friends came to tea.

Trace over **q**. Then write **q**.

Write **q** to begin each word.
Draw a line from the picture to the picture word.

_____ uilt

_____ ueen

_____ uail

r

rocket

Trace over r. Then write r.

r

Write r to finish the picture words.

_ake

bi_d

r

was a **rabbit**

With fur soft and white;

He escaped from his hutch

And hopped out of sight.

Trace over r. Then write r.

r

Write r to begin two words. Write r to end a word.
Draw a line from the picture to the picture word.

_____ ake

_____ ose

sta _____

s
seal

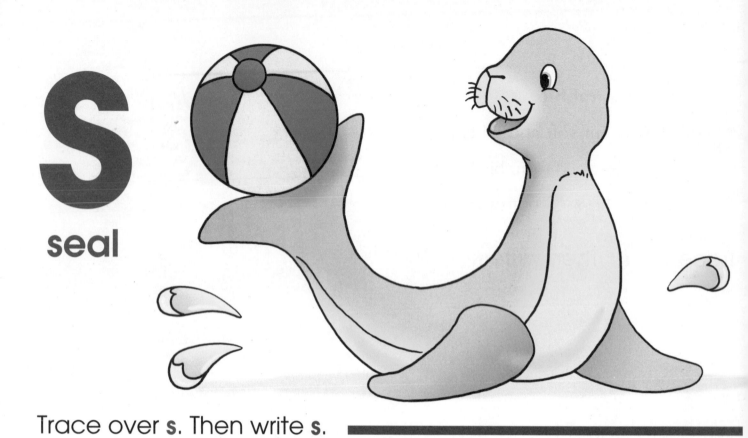

Trace over **s**. Then write **s**.

s

Write **s** to finish the picture words.

un

va e

S was a **snowman**

With an orange carrot nose;

Although it was cold,

He never wore clothes.

Trace over **s**. Then write **s**.

S

Write **s** to begin two words. Write **s** to end a word.
Draw a line from the picture to the picture word.

_____un

_____ocks

boot_____

t

turtle

Trace over t. Then write t.

1
2

Write t to finish the picture words.

op

ba

t

was a **tortoise**

With a shell red and black;

Friends played checkers

On top of her back.

Trace over t. Then write t.

Write t to begin two words. Write t to end a word.
Draw a line from the picture to the picture word.

_____ urtle

_____ urkey

ca _____

u

umbrellas

Trace over **u**. Then write **u**.

Write **u** to finish the picture words.

___ p

___ b ___ g

u

was an **umbrella**

That turned upside down;

It filled up with rain,

And ducks swam around.

Trace over **u**. Then write **u**.

¹∪²↓

Write **u** to begin each word.
Draw a line from the picture to the picture word.

_____ p

_____ nderwear

_____ nicorn

V
valentines

Trace over **v**. Then write **v**.

Write **v** to finish the picture words.

fi_ve

ri_er

44

V

V was a **violin**

That had a bad squeak;

It gave you a headache

That lasted a week.

Trace over **v**. Then write **v**.

Write **v** to begin each word.
Draw a line from the picture to the picture word.

_____ an

_____ ase

_____ olcano

W

watermelon

Trace over **w**. Then write **w**.

Write **w** to finish the picture words.

  orm

 co

W

was a **whale**

Who sailed for the stars,

Refuelled and ate lunch

At the café on Mars.

Trace over w. Then write w.

1 2 3 4

W

Write w to begin two words. Write w to end a word.
Draw a line from the picture to the picture word.

_____ ave

_____ olf

co _____

X

x-ray

Trace over **x**. Then write **x**.

Write **x** to finish the picture words.

fo

si

48

X

was an **x-ray**
With film black and white;
It showed things inside me
That were not quite right.

Trace over **x**. Then write **x**.

Write **x** to begin one word. Write **x** to end two words.
Draw a line from the picture to the picture word.

_____ -ray

bo _____

fo _____

y

yachts

Trace over y. Then write y.

Write y to finish the picture words.

o–yo

ak

50

y was a **yo-yo**

That rolled on the floor;

The string wasn't broken,

It was out to explore.

Trace over **y**. Then write **y**.

¹y²

Write **y** to begin two words. Write **y** to end a word.
Draw a line from the picture to the picture word.

_____ o-yo

_____ acht

ha _____

Z

zip

Trace over **z**. Then write **z**.

Write **z** to finish the picture words.

ero

ebra

Z

was a **zeppelin**

That flew through the sky,

While its crew of three monkeys

Ate hot apple pie.

Trace over **z**. Then write **z**.

Write **z** to begin each word.
Draw a line from the picture to the picture word.

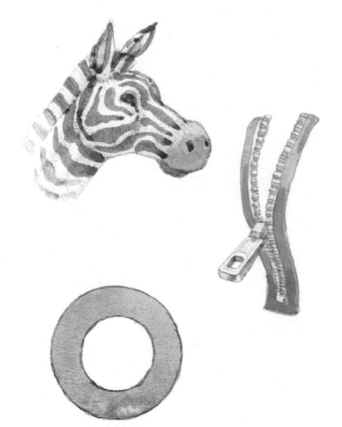

_____ ero

_____ ebra

_____ ip

Trace the letter. Say the name of each letter.

Write the correct **letter** to finish each picture word.

e d r

b ll

bi d

og

Write the correct **letter** to finish each picture word.

p a h

c a t

m o g

h o o k

Write the correct **letter** to finish each picture word.

c m o

frog

drum

car

Write the correct **letter** to finish each picture word.

i s b

bear

fish

horse

Write the correct **letter** to finish each picture word.

w u l

bug

Lion

cow

Sun can see what swims in the sea!

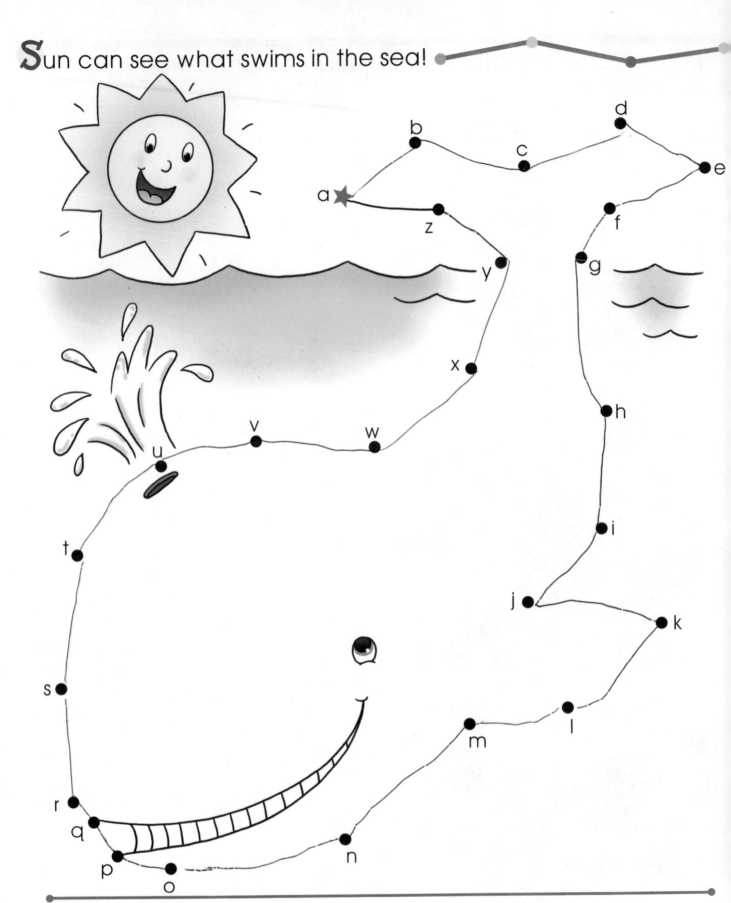

Join the dots from **a** to **z**. Start at the star ★.
Then colour the rest of the picture.

Who is in a muddle as he sits in a puddle?

Join the dots from **a** to **z**. Start at the star ★.
Then colour the rest of the picture.

The sun shines bright to flowers' delight!

Join the dots from **a** to **z**. Start at the star ★.
Then colour the rest of the picture.

Whenever you see animals gathered like this, they're trying to say something! Write the first letter of each picture name.

Find and circle each letter.

AB CITY